The Sing Song

Written by Roderick Hunt
Illustrations by Nick Schon, based on
the original characters created by
Roderick Hunt and Alex Brychta

OXFORD
UNIVERSITY PRESS

Read these words

si**ng**	so**ng**
di**ng**	lo**ng**
alo**ng**	sa**ng**
ro**ck**	sho**ck**

"It is a Sing Song," said Dad.

"Let's go to the Sing Song," said Dad.

"Yes, let's go along to it," said Mum.

They went to the Sing Song.

They met Wilf and Wilma.

Wilf and Wilma sang a song.
They had fun singing it.

Kipper had a song to sing.

Mum sang it with him.

Biff and Chip sang a song.

Such a sad song.

It was a sad song.

Dad sang a song.

It went on and on.

Dad sang and sang.

Dad won the Sing Song.

Talk about the story

Who did the family meet at the Sing Song?

What song did Kipper sing?

Why were Biff and Chip surprised that Dad won?

What do you like to sing?

Spot the difference

Find the five differences in the two pictures of Dad.